The *Cartier* Museum
at The Goldsmiths' Hall
Foster Lane
London

Exhibition
23rd May - 10th June 1988

Cartier
Joaillier - Orfèvre
13, Rue de la Paix
Paris.
Londres   New-York
175-176, New Bond St.   653, Fifth Avenue

Paris
1847

London
1902

New York
1909

Jacques-Théodule Cartier (1884-1942)

175–176 New Bond Street – LONDON

3

THE CARTIER MUSEUM

The rare pieces of jewellery and works of art of the museum have been collected over years in Cartier's spirit for tradition. Today, they can be looked at as the legacy of a company with roots back to some 150 years.

Joseph Kanouï, Chairman of Cartier, had already kept up with great interest the author's, Hans Nadelhoffer, jewellery expert and Christie's Geneva's president, finalization of his book "Cartier - Jewellers Extraordinary". Such volume retraces extensively and richly illustrates Cartier's fascinating history from 1847 onwards to our present days.
Thanks to the museum, the company is proud to illustrate three-dimensionally their jeweller's art, so rich of tradition, inventions and successive fashion trends.

When the "Cartier Foundation for Contemporary Art" at Jouy-en-Josas, near Versailles, was inaugurated in 1983, the dynamic international firm intended to cast a glance over its past. Alain D. Perrin, the forward-thinking president of Cartier International and patron of contemporary art, set his heart on the project to make this collection accessible to clients and friends.

The basic elements to the museum had already been laid by the conspicuous, responsible directors of the main office in Paris and the affiliates in London and New York: since ever, they have repurchased Cartier's early creations from different reasons, without any intention whatsoever to transform or resell them but to put them respectfully in banksafes. During 1983/84, these selected works of art were brought together and catalogued by Cartier Geneva.

The collection, which includes today more than 500 originally numbered and signed pieces, comes from well-known estates, international art trade and historical auctions. The reason why it is exceptional is due to the fact that it refers to one, today still existing jeweller – in comparison and contrary to Carl Fabergé.

The precious collection, the value of which is difficult to stipulate, is also rare because all models can be identified and dated thanks to the nearly complete archives – which had been wisely transferred from Paris to London during the last World War. Also the handwritten order and store books as well as the sketch and photograph albums throw further light on each piece's history. Such are so voluminous that in Paris, London and New York one archivist is fully employed to safe-keep on microfilms the past and present data for deposit in banksafes.

Furthermore, the very orderly correspondence with clients allows precious guidances as for instance on the negotiations undertaken by the three Cartier brothers of historical diamonds, colour stones and pearls. The Cartier chronologist, Gilberte Gautier, had found the inspiration for her book "13, rue de la Paix" from such abundant exchange of letters.

The Cartier Museum includes gem-set jewels, which, until circa 1890, were still traditionally mounted in silver. Pieces from the Garland Style, after 1900, show the aesthetically revolutionary and successful use of a naturally white, non-oxyding precious metal: platinum was employed by Louis Cartier (1875-1942) after long experimentation firstly and for ever in the jeweller's art.

Realistically carved animals and flowers of jade, lapislazuli, agate, quartz, etc. are embellished with precious woods and enamelled gold and remind us of the competition to Fabergé in St. Petersburg where, in 1908, Cartier opened a shop temporarily.

A multitude of table and travelling clocks, bracelet and pocket watches impress us with their technical achievements and abundance of ideas as well as with their varieties of avant-garde shapes and colour combinations.

In addition, there are several "mystery clocks": the earliest elegant model of 1913, the "porticus" and "screen" as well as the "chimaera" examples. The latter is one out of the twelve rare masterpieces realized by Cartier between 1922 and 1931, which incorporate as a nucleus a jade or an agate animal mostly Chinese 19th century. The chimaera carries a totally transparent and geometrically-cut crystal, artfully mounted, in the centre of which the hands seem to revolve magically. Such time-pieces, harmoniously uniting in one object the highest technical skill and expression of fertile imagination, deserve without doubt the denomination "objet d'art".

Necklaces, bracelets, ear-pendants, rings and cuff-links in the Art Deco style are very often set with baguette-cut diamonds. This cut is another invention of Louis-Joseph Cartier, the most adept of the three brothers.

Accessories, such as frames, belt buckles, ink-stands and pens, agenda bindings, perfume flasks, lorgnettes and glasses, powder and cigarette cases, cigarette lighters and gem-set evening bags – many from the "twenties" and inspired by Egyptian, Persian or Far Eastern influences, are precursors of the "Les Must de Cartier".

The technique of "invisible mounting" – or "mysterious-setting" – so called after the clocks containing invisible movements, was already patented by Cartier in 1933. A sapphire and diamond brooch in the form of a rose blossom illustrates this extremely delicate art of gem-setting in "invisible claws".

Many famous and well-known names are linked to the jewels and objects present of the museum: King Farouk of Egypt, Mary Queen of the Serbes, The Aga Khan, King of Nepal, Miss Barbara Hutton, Mrs. Donahue, Madame Coty, Alexander King of Jugoslavia, Countess Mona Bismarck, Countess Olga von Hohenfelsen, etc. From the estate of the Duchess of Windsor, bequeathed to the Research Institute Pasteur in Paris and auctioned at Sotheby's Geneva in Spring 1987, two rare pieces were acquired: a platinum brooch set with brilliant-cut diamonds and sapphires in the form of a realistic modelled panther seated on a circular 150-carat cabochon sapphire: it was realized on special order from this extravagant client in 1948 – as was the tiger-lorgnette of 1954 – by Jeanne Toussaint (1887-1978), Cartier's brilliant jewellery creator and one of Coco Chanel's friends.

The panther appears for the first time in 1914 on a watch, then, in 1928, as a relief on a black lacquer powder case. It has become Cartier's symbol through many successive creations.

From the French President, Edgar Faure, comes a model of the world-known "Tank" bracelet watches of 1970, which marks symbolically the passage to Cartier's presence.

For the time being, the Cartier collection has no fixed abode, and the museum itself might later possibly be on exhibition at the Cartier Foundation. However, in the meantime, several proposals for exhibition have been accepted from international museums and galleries. So far, Cartier had already organised several differently selected exhibitions, as for instance at the County Museum in Los Angeles, the Villa Stuck in Munich, the Petit Palais in Geneva, the French Embassy in Tokyo, the Biblioteca Trivulziana of the Castello Sforzesco in Milan, the Art Gallery in Vancouver and the Fermoy Foundation at King's Lynn.

Eric Nussbaum
Directeur Cartier Haute Joaillerie, Geneva
Curator of the Cartier Museum

Cartier Jewellers
thank
Mr. Wafik Rida Said
for the kind loan of
The Duchess of Windsor's jewels
from his personal collection

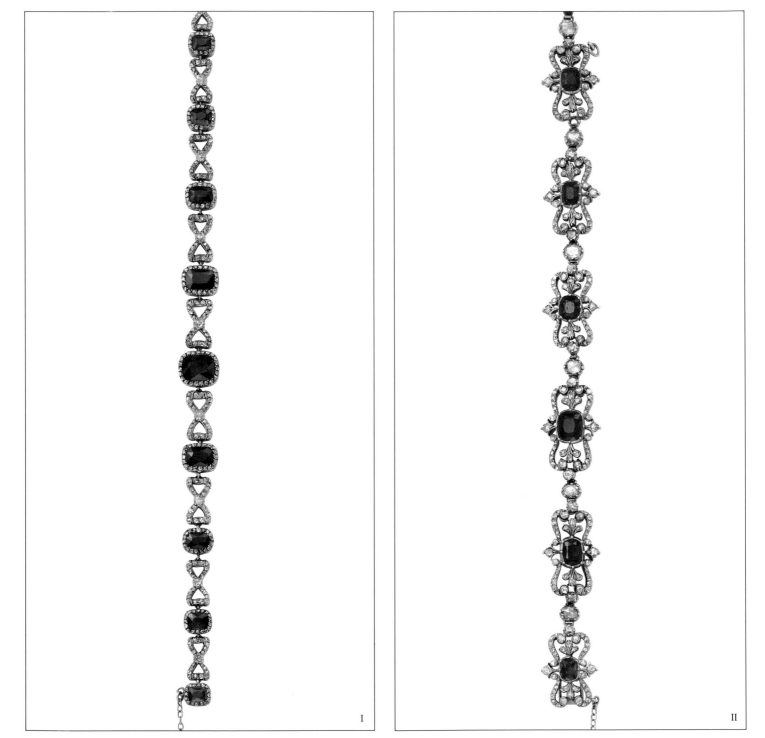

I

II

1. *Bracelet*, 1899
silver
sapphires, diamonds
ILLUSTRATION I

2. *Bracelet*, 1899
silver
rubies, diamonds
ILLUSTRATION II

3. *Watch pendant*, 1900
gold, enamel, porcelaine plaque
diamonds

4. *Bracelet*, 1907
gold
rubies, diamonds, pearls
Provenance: Nageb Pacha

5. *Bangle*, 1907
platinum
diamonds

6. *Bangle*, 1907
gold
rubies, diamonds

* 7. *Brooch*, 1907
in form of a Japanese knot
platinum, gold
diamonds, rubies

8. *Pocket watch*, 1908
gold, enamel
diamonds

* As early as 1906, Louis Cartier encouraged the designers to switch from the traditional Louis XVI forms to more abstract designs using "calibré-cut" colour stones in ornamental patterns leading to the later Art-Deco style.

III

IV

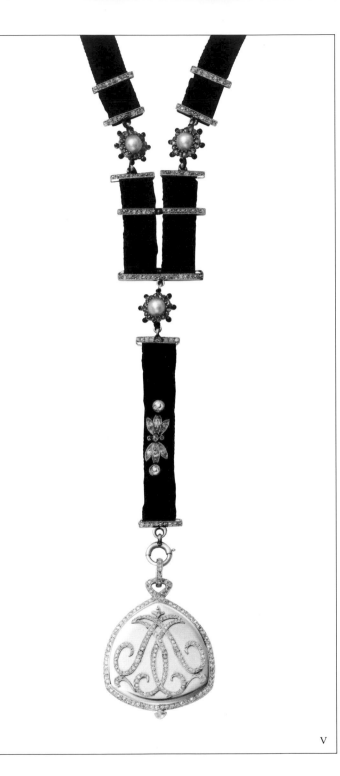

V

* 9. <u>*Tea and coffee service*</u>, *circa 1880*
silver

10. <u>*Bow-brooch*</u>, *1910*
platinum
pearls, diamonds
ILLUSTRATION IV

11. <u>*Brooch*</u>, *1913*
platinum
diamonds, pearls
ILLUSTRATION III

12. <u>*Pendant watch*</u>, *1910*
platinum, gold
diamonds, pearls
ILLUSTRATION V

13. <u>*Pocket watch*</u>, *"eclipse", 1910*
gold, enamel

14. <u>*Lady's bracelet watch*</u>, *1912*
platinum, gold
diamonds, pearls, onyx
Provenance: Princess Orloff

15. <u>*Gentleman's wrist watch "tonneau"*</u>, *1913*
gold
sapphire crown

16. <u>*Lady's wrist watch*</u>, *circa 1913*
platinum
diamonds, onyx

17. <u>*Lady's wrist watch*</u>, *1914*
platinum
diamonds

18. <u>*Lady's wrist watch*</u>, *circa 1915*
platinum, gold
diamonds, onyx

* A similar tea-service was commissioned in 1859 by the Empress Eugénie, spouse of Napoleon III.

Louis-Joseph Cartier (1875-1942)

13, rue de la Paix — PARIS

PLATINUM

The archives mention platinum as early as in 1853. But it took about 50 years to find a suitable alloy which permitted the use of it for setting diamonds.

The successful introduction by Cartier of this precious metal – already known in ancient Egypt –, to replace the oxyding silver, meant a great aesthetic revolution in jewellery.

CARTIER HALLMARKS

1846

1903

1912

1919

1922

1929

1973

1980

VI

VII

19. *Tiara, circa 1905*
in form of a scrolled wreath
platinum
diamonds
ILLUSTRATION VI

20. *Lavallière, circa 1907*
platinum
diamonds

21. *Stomacher brooch, 1907*
in form of a double ribbon bow
platinum
diamonds
Provenance: de Beaumont
ILLUSTRATION VII

22. *Brooch, 1913*
in form of two attached circles
platinum
diamonds

23. *Pendant brooch, 1913*
platinum
Conch pearl, pearls, diamonds

24. *Pair of haircomb ornaments, 1910*
platinum
diamonds

25. *Pendant watch, circa 1905*
platinum, enamelled gold
diamonds

26. *Pendant watch, circa 1910*
platinum
diamonds
pearl and diamond chain

27. *Pocket watch, circa 1913*
platinum
sapphires, diamonds

28. *Bracelet watch, 1910*
platinum
diamonds
platinum curb chain
Provenance: Princesse Murat

29. *Watch brooch, 1912*
platinum
diamonds, rock-crystal

30. *Desk clock, circa 1910*
square agate plaque
gold, enamel
diamonds

VIII

IX

16

31. <u>*Choker*</u>, *circa 1910*
platinum
diamonds

32. <u>*Necklace*</u>, *1911*
platinum
diamonds, pearls
Provenance: Comte de Bourbon-Busset

33. <u>*Stomacher brooch*</u>, *circa 1907*
platinum
diamonds, pearls

34. <u>*Pendant necklace*</u>, *1909*
platinum
emeralds, diamonds, pearls
Illustration IX

35. <u>*Pair of earpendants*</u>, *1919*
platinum
yellow sapphires, diamonds, pearls,
onyx
Illustration VIII

36. <u>*Sudanese bangle*</u>, *1919*
ivory, gold, enamel
coral, diamonds

37. <u>*Lapel watch*</u>, *1919*
platinum
diamonds, onyx
moiré silk ribbon

38. <u>*Lady's bracelet watch*</u>, *1909*
gold, enamel
sapphires
moiré silk ribbon

39. <u>*Lady's bracelet watch*</u>, *1913*
platinum
diamonds
Milanese platinum bracelet

40. <u>*Lady's bracelet watch*</u>, *1912*
platinum
diamonds, onyx

41. <u>*Lady's bracelet watch*</u>, *1913*
platinum
diamonds

42. <u>*Lady's bracelet watch*</u>, *1914*
platinum
diamonds

43. <u>*Lady's bracelet watch*</u>, *1918*
platinum
diamonds

44. <u>*Pocket watch*</u>, *circa 1910*
platinum
sapphires

45. <u>*"Taxi" pocket watch*</u>, *circa 1912*
platinum
sapphires

46. <u>*Desk clock with easel*</u>, *1914*
rock-crystal, ebonite
gold, enamel
diamonds

At the turn of the century, two opposing trends ruled the jewellery design. The goldsmiths and "orfèvres-bijoutiers" subscribed to the Art-Nouveau style in asymmetrical, soft lines - inspired by nature - and using new materials, such as horn, ivory and celluloid synthetics. The jewellers, instead, were favouring the elegant Garland style, a revival of the Louis XVI one, the leader of which was Louis Cartier. Therefore only a few examples of Art-Nouveau creations are registered in the archives before 1900, and then, during World War I, some others of principally religious and martial motifs.

47. _Mantle clock_, 1904
    in form of a trophy
    marble, silver-gilt, enamel

48. _Mantle clock,,_ 1904
    in form of a trophy
    marble, silver-gilt, enamel
    Provenance: Marquis de Breteuil

49. _Desk clock_, 1907
    gold, silver, enamel
    sapphire crown

50. _Desk clock / Barometer_, 1908
    in form of a cylinder
    gold, silver-gilt, enamel
    diamonds

51. _Repeating desk clock_, 1908
    gold, enamel
    diamonds, agate, moonstone pushpiece
    ILLUSTRATION X

52. _Desk clock_, 1908
    gold, enamel
    diamonds, agate
    Provenance: Duchess of Marlborough
    ILLUSTRATION XI

53. _Repeating desk clock_, 1909
    gold, silver, enamel
    diamonds, sapphires, moonstone, agate

54. _Desk clock with easel_, 1909
    silver, silver-gilt, enamel,
    diamonds

55. _Miniature desk clock_, circa 1910
    silver, silver-gilt, enamel
    diamonds, agate

56. _Desk clock with easel_, 1912
    gold, silver, enamel
    diamonds
    Provenance: Comtesse de Hohenfelsen

57. _Repeating desk clock_, circa 1920
    gold, enamel
    diamonds, onyx, moonstone pushpiece

58. _Desk clock with easel_, 1919
    gold, silver, enamel
    diamonds

59. _Pendant watch_, 1907
    platinum, enamel
    diamonds
    ribbon sautoir

60. _Pocket watch with chain_, 1909
    gold, enamel
    diamonds, pearls

61. _Pendant watch with chain_, 1910
    platinum, gold, enamel
    diamonds, pearls

62. _Pendant watch with chain_, circa 1910
    gold, enamel
    diamonds, pearls

63. _"Hunter" pendant watch_, circa 1910
    platinum, gold enamel
    diamonds

64. _Fob watch_, 1911
    gold, enamel
    diamonds, sapphires

65. _Pocket watch_, 1908
    gold, enamel
    sapphires

66. _Ink-pen with cap_, circa 1909
    gold, enamel

67. _Telescopic seal pencil with cap_, circa 1912
    gold, enamel
    diamonds, onyx

68. _Scent-flask_, 1912
    gold, silver, silver-gilt, enamel
    diamonds

Louis Cartier's negative attitude towards Art-Nouveau jewellery enabled him to move naturally from the geometrical patterns of the Garland style to the more linear Art-Deco design.

Empress Eugénie (1826-1920)
The Spanish born Eugenia Maria de Montijo de Guzman, spouse of Napoleon III, became client at Cartier's in 1859.

The Countess of Nieuwekerke, wife of the bronze sculptor, later appointed superintendent of Fine Arts by Napoleon III and the Princess Mathilde, daughter of Napoleon's brother Jerôme, were possibly instigating the Empress to become a client, and thus she fulfilled Louis-François Cartier's wish to become a purveyor to the Imperial Court.

St. Petersburg

After the Paris exhibition of Russian art by Diaghilev in 1906, Cartier had organised the year after their first successful exhibition at the Hotel d'Europe in Saint Petersburg, where then, in 1908, a temporary branch was opened at 28, quai de la Cour. In 1912 the Paris City Council presented Nicolas II with an Egg in the Russian Style commissioned at Cartier's. The competition to Carl Fabergé, of French origin also, was evident, since both jewellers created multitudes of "objets d'art", mainly in the Louis XVI style with enamels of the most extraordinary perfection and striking colours.

XII

XIII

XIV

69. *Powder compact*, 1909
    gold, enamel
    mauve jade
    Provenance: Grande Duchesse Xenia

70. *Pin cushion*, 1907
    gold, silver, enamel

71. *Umbrella handle with watch*, circa 1905
    gold, enamel, diamonds

72. *Lily-of-the-Valley*, 1908
    gold
    opal, quartz, agate, ivory
    ILLUSTRATION XIV

73. *Resting pig*, 1911
    rose quartz
    diamond
    ILLUSTRATION XII

74. *Couple of budgerigars*, circa 1910
    gold
    diamonds, quartz, ivory
    ILLUSTRATION XIII

75. *Pair of parakeets*, 1927
    gold
    quartz, agate, ivory

76. *King Charles spaniel*, circa 1925
    gold, enamel, jade
    sapphires, diamonds

77. *Mantle clock*, 1907
    in form of an urn
    gold, silver, enamel
    diamonds, sapphire

78. *Desk clock with calendar support*, 1908
    gold, enamel
    diamonds, moonstones
    ILLUSTRATION XV

79. *Mantle clock*, 1908
    in form of a drum on pillar
    gold, silver, enamel
    diamonds, agate

80. *Desk clock*, 1910
    gold, silver, enamel
    diamonds, agate

81. *Desk clock, with easel*, 1913
    silver, enamel
    diamonds
    ILLUSTRATION XVI

82. *Desk clock*, 1920
    gold, silver, enamel
    diamonds, agate
    ILLUSTRATION XVII

83. *Repeating desk clock*, 1910
    gold, enamel
    diamonds, agate

84. *Repeating desk clock*, 1910
    gold, enamel
    diamonds, agate, moonstone

85. *Repeating desk clock*, 1910
    gold, silver, enamel
    diamonds, agate, moonstone

86. *Repeating desk clock*, circa 1910
    gold, silver, enamel
    diamonds, agate, amethyst

87. *Repeating desk clock*, 1911
    gold, silver, enamel
    diamonds, agate, amethyst

88. *Repeating desk clock*, 1915
    gold, enamel
    diamonds, agate

XV

XVI

XVII

89. *Desk clock with easel*, 1920
    arch-shaped rock-crystal plaque
    gold, enamel
    diamonds

90. *Desk clock with easel, circa 1920*
    arch-shaped rock-crystal plaque
    gold, enamel
    diamonds

91. *Desk clock with easel*, 1924
    arch-shaped rock-crystal plaque
    gold, enamel
    diamonds

92. *Desk clock with easel*, 1924
    arch-shaped rock-crystal plaque
    gold, enamel
    diamonds

93. *Ball watch pendant with chain*, 1905
    gold, enamel
    diamonds, pearls

94. *Pendant watch with chain*, 1908
    gold, enamel
    diamonds, pearls

95. *Pendant watch with chain, circa 1910*
    platinum, silver, enamel
    diamonds, pearls

96. *Pendant watch with chain, circa 1912*
    multi-colour gold, enamel
    diamonds, pearls

97. *Cigarette case*, 1907
    gold, enamel
    diamonds

98. *Cigarette case, circa 1910*
    gold, enamel
    diamonds

99. *Cigarette case*, 1912
    multi-colour gold
    sapphire

100. *Pocket watch*, 1910
     two-colour gold

101. *Pair of cuff-links*, 1910
     gold, enamel

102. *Pocket knife, circa 1905*
     gold, enamel

103. *Folding lorgnette*, 1906
     gold, enamel
     diamonds

104. *Belt buckle*, 1906
     transforms to a brooch
     gold, enamel
     diamonds

105. *Desk barometer with easel*, 1908
     gold, silver, enamel, ivory

106. *Letter opener*, 1906
     gold, silver, enamel
     ivory

107. *Miniature frame, circa 1910*
     in form of a camera
     multi-colour gold, enamel
     ruby

108. *Desk frame with easel, circa 1910*
     nephrite hoop
     gold, silver, enamel

109. *Letter opener*, 1913
     gold, enamel, nephrite
     sapphires
     Provenance: H.H. The Aga Khan

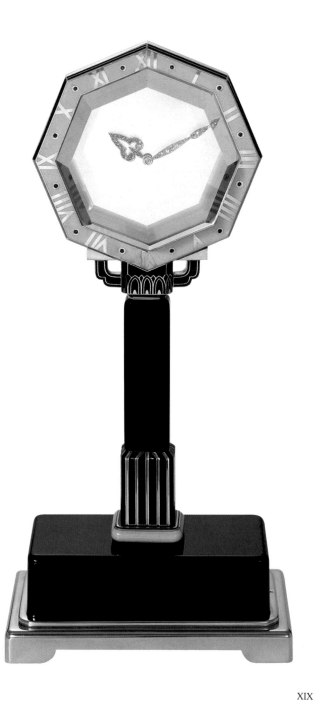

XVIII

XIX

* 110. *Mystery clock, "A" model, circa 1920*
    shaped rectangular faceted rock-crystal case, applied gold and white enamel garland front frame enclosing circular gold and white enamel Roman chapters, dial surround with diamonds, fancy diamond hands, rectangular onyx plinth on flat gold feet, four diamond corner ornaments.
    ILLUSTRATION XVIII

* 111. *Mystery clock, "A" model, circa 1925*
    shaped rectangular faceted rock-crystal case, applied gold and white enamel garland front frame enclosing circular gold and white enamel Roman chapter and rosace hoop with interior diamond border, scrolled diamond hands, rectangular onyx plinth set with four diamond corners, four flat feet.

** 112. *Mystery clock, 1921*
    octagonal faceted rock-crystal case, openwork faceted diamond spade hands, gold and turquoise enamel Roman chapter and rosace bezel, oblong onyx and gold pillar from turquoise enamel surround, rectangular onyx pedestal on gold plinth
    ILLUSTRATION XIX

* The first mystery clock "modèle A" of 1913 works on a double-axle system. According to the archives, the first one made was sold to J.P. Morgan, Jr. A similar creation of 1924 went to H.M. The Queen Mary. And a model with a lapis-lazuli base was offered by the Général de Gaulle, then head of the French Provisional Government, to Stalin.

** A second model of the mystery clock, using one single central axle, was created in 1920 and was subject to variations using octagonal shaped dials or round faceted hugh citrines increasing the mystery of the function.

∗∗113. _Mystery clock_, circa 1921
_octagonal faceted rock-crystal dial,
applied with double diamond circles enclos-
ing diamond Roman chapters, openwork diamond spade hands, gold, black and turquoise
enamel palmette pattern bezel, short gold and
black enamel support embellished with four
cabochon turquoises, rectangular onyx support on gold and black enamel scrolled plinth._

∗∗114. _Mystery clock_, 1925
_octagonal faceted rock-crystal dial, black
Roman chapters, diamond serpent hands,
gold and black enamel meander-pattern bezel
with triple cabochon turquoise corner motifs,
short gold and black enamel support, rectangular onyx pedestal, gold and black enamel
meander pattern plinth._

∗∗115. _Mystery clock_, 1926
_octagonal faceted rock-crystal dial, scrolled
diamond hands, gold and black enamel bezel
with applied diamond Roman chapters, carved coral exterior rim, short gold and black
enamel support set with four cabochon corals,
rectangular onyx pedestal with diamond
letter "F" flanked by diamond wings, rectangular onyx and gold plinth set with coral
baton and gold arrow ornament._
Provenance: King Farouk of Egypt
ILLUSTRATION XX

∗∗∗116. _Mystery clock_, "screen", 1923
_rectangular gold and black enamel case,
baton jade top and bottom line in onyx tube
surround, central rock-crystal disc, fancy
diamond hands, diamond bezel, gold and
white enamel Roman chapter and rosace
hoop, gold, black enamel and diamond corners,
lateral onyx half-hoop supports and central
onyx sphere, rectangular jade pedestal, step-
cut gold and onyx plinth._

ILLUSTRATION XXI

∗∗∗ A third model, the "écran" or "screen" appeared in 1923. From the movement, hidden in the base, a single central axle
carries the motive power through a hollow sphere to the dial.

117. *Mystery clock, "portico", 1923*
in form of a Buddhist temple gong gate
dodecagonal faceted rock-crystal dial, scrolled
diamond hands, gold and black enamel bezel,
diamond Roman chapters, gold and black
enamel suspension ornament from rock-
crystal bar, rock-crystal, onyx and gold gate
columns, onyx capital, coral embellishments,
onyx cube pillar bases adorned with step-cut
rock-crystal wedges, flat gold plinth, carved
rock-crystal Billiken seated on gate top.
Provenance: Mrs H. McCormick
ILLUSTRATION XXII

In the year 1923-1925, only six Oriental-style "portico" (gateway) models were made, containing the movement in the span:

1923 dodecagonal dial in crystal with a "Billiken", the Anglo Saxon Buddha-like god of the underworld and of plenty.

1924 octagonal dial in crystal with square pillars

1924 dodecagonal dial with square rose quartz pillars and two Buddhist lions

1924 dodecagonal dial in crystal with Buddhist lion (the head to the right)

1924 dodecagonal dial in crystal with a Buddha

1925 dodecagonal dial in crystal with a Buddhist lion (the head to the left)

118. *Mystery clock, "Chimera", 1924*
engraved agate chimera with mouth chain (Chinese, 19th century) pared with gold, turquoise, white and black enamel saddle seat, pearl fringes, topped with hexagonal clock: hexagonal faceted rock-crystal dial, diamond dragon hands, mother-of-pearl bezel, applied diamond Roman chapters accentuated by black enamel surround, gold, turquoise and black enamel dial rim, similar exterior bezel rim embellished with pearls and turquoises, the chimera riding on rose quartz waves with shells on rectangular quartz plaque, rectangular gold, black enamel and mother-of-pearl mosaic pedestal embellished with multi-enamel and gold dragons, four lapis-lazuli ball feet.

ILLUSTRATION XXIII

119. *Mystery clock, 1931*
"Chinese Goddess and Fu Dog",
carved white jade statue of Chinese goddess Kuan Yin (Chinese, 19th century) behind mystery clock: octagonal faceted rock-crystal dial, diamond dragon hands, gold, turquoise and blue enamel bezel with diamond Roman chapters, deity and clock supported by tripod carved jade pedestal set with coral, pearls, gold, black, blue and turquoise enamel top embellishments flanked by Chinese jade dog Fu with coral rose and by carved jade cylinder vase with coral branches and pearls, rectangular onyx base, top pearl line and scrolled gold, blue and turquoise enamel bottom line.
Provenance: Mr. Paul-Louis Weiller

In the years 1922-1931, twelve Chinese mystery clocks were created:

1922 Jade Mandarin Duck

1924 Agate Chimera I (see 118 ill. XXIII)

1925 Two Jade Carps: with a dial of the concept of Grollier de Sevières (not a mystery clock)

1925 Jade Vase with bird and flower

1925 Crystal Turtle

1925 Agate Chimera II with round citrine dial

1926 Chinese Goddess Kuan Yin

1927 Crystal Chimera

1928 Jade Elephant

1929 Jade Buddhist Lions

1930 Coral Chimera

1931 Jade Chimera Goddess Kuan Yin, movement with striking chimes (see 119)

The vase and the animals are all Chinese carvings of the 19th century.

XXIV

XXV

XXVI

120. *Gentleman's wrist watch*, "Santos", 1919
gold case, sapphire crown
ILLUSTRATION XXIV

121. *Gentleman's wrist watch*, "Santos", 1928
gold case, sapphire crown

122. *Pocket lighter*, 1913
gold, enamel
diamonds

123. *Pocket lighter*, circa 1921
gold, enamel
onyx

124. *Pocket lighter*, 1928
inset with a watch
gold, enamel
Provenance: Roger Sauerbach

125. *Pocket lighter*, 1928
gold
diamonds
Provenance: Duchess Olga Kahn

126. *Pocket lighter*, circa 1930
gold cylinder

127. *Cigarette case*, 1923
multi-colour gold
sapphire
Provenance: H.M. The King of Yugoslavia

128. *Cigarette case*, 1925
gold, enamel
diamonds

129. *Cigarette case*, 1927
multi-colour gold
sapphires

130. *Cigarette case*, 1927
gold, enamel
diamond

131. *Cigarette case*, 1927
gold, enamel, lacquer

132. *Cigarette case*, 1928
gold
interior inscription

133. *Cigarette case*, 1928
gold, enamel
diamonds, rubies, jade

134. *Agenda cover*, 1928
gold, silver

135. *Cigarette holder*, 1923
gold, amber, jet
ruby, sapphire, emerald, topaz, amethyst

136. *Cigarette holder*, 1927
jade, ivory
sapphires, diamonds

137. *Cigarette holder*, 1929
platinum, amber
diamonds, sapphires

138. *Desk clock with easel*, 1920
arch-shaped onyx plaque
platinum, gold, enamel
diamonds

139. *Dress pocket watch*, circa 1926
gold, enamel
rock-crystal

140. *Dress pocket watch*, circa 1927
gold, enamel
rock-crystal

141. *Desk clock*, circa 1927
marble, silver,
tortoiseshell
ILLUSTRATION XXVI

142. *Presentation cigarette case*, 1929
gold, silver, enamel
onyx
Provenance: Mr. P.C. Mérillon

TANK – SHOWCASE 8

143. *Gentleman's bracelet watch "Tank"*, 1925
gold case and link bracelet
sapphire

144. *Gentleman's bracelet watch "Tank"*, 1934
platinum case and link bracelet
sapphire
Provenance: The Prince of Nepal
ILLUSTRATION XXV

145. *Gentleman's wrist watch "Tank"*, 1924
platinum, gold
sapphire

146. *Gentleman's wrist watch "Tank"*, 1936
gold
sapphire

147. *Gentleman's wrist watch*, circa 1915
platinum
diamond

148. *Desk clock with easel*, circa 1914
arch-shaped onyx plaque
gold, enamel
diamonds

149. *Vanity case*, 1924
gold, enamel
diamonds

150. *Vanity case*, 1927
gold, enamel
diamonds, sapphires, jade
Provenance: Baron Ed. de Rothschild

151. *Cigarette case*, 1925
gold, enamel
Provenance: Jeanne Toussaint

152. *Cigarette case and lighter*, 1928
gold, enamel
emeralds, diamonds, moonstones

153. *Vanity case*, 1929
gold, enamel
diamonds

154. *Vanity case*, 1929
gold, enamel
diamonds
Provenance: F. L. Hutton

155. *Vanity case*, 1933
gold, enamel
diamonds
Provenance: E. Dubonnet

156. *Vanity case*, 1933
gold, enamel
Provenance: A. Tardy

157. *Cigarette case*, 1925
rock-crystal
gold, enamel
diamonds
Provenance: Jacques Carmona

158. *Pencil holder with seal*, 1924
gold, enamel
Provenance: W. A. Moore

159. *Pencil holder*, circa 1925
gold

160. *Ink-pen with calendar cap*, circa 1925
gold, enamel

161. *Dress pocket watch*, circa 1920
onyx case, gold

162. *Dress pocket watch*, circa 1926
circular onyx case, platinum, gold
diamonds

163. *Pair of cuff-links*, 1925
platinum
onyx, diamonds

164. *Pair of cuff-links*, 1931
platinum
sapphires

Mercredi

Mon cher Ami

Voulez vous dîner avec
moi demain ? J'ai aussi
invité Tissandier et Peyrey
Le rendez-vous est au 150
Champs Elysées à 8¼.
Votre Ami
A. Santos-Dumont

Alberto Santos Dumont (1873-1932), aviator and friend of Louis-Joseph Cartier,
for whom the famous wrist watch was created in 1911: "Santos"

The armoured cars of the Allies and by Renault of World War I gave the name to another famous Cartier watch in 1919: "Tank"

165. _Line bracelet_, 1920
platinum
diamonds, onyx

166. _Pendant brooch_, 1920
platinum
diamonds, sapphires, onyx

167. _Pendant_, circa 1920
in form of a stylised flower arrangement
platinum
sapphires, diamonds

168. _Jabot pin_, 1920
in form of an arch-shaped shield
platinum
sapphires, diamonds, coral, onyx
Provenance: Mrs. C. Wilson

169. _Belt buckle_, 1922
in form of two onyx hoops
platinum, gold
cabochon turquoise, diamonds, onyx

170. _Lipstick holder_, 1924
gold, enamel
onyx
made for Guerlain

171. _Folding lorgnette_, circa 1925
gold, enamel

172. _Vanity case_, 1920
oval cased
gold, enamel
diamonds
interior amber cigarette holder

173. _Vanity case_, 1920
oval cased, suspension ring and chain
gold, enamel, lacquer
diamonds
interior black amber cigarette holder

174. _Vanity case_, 1922
oval cased, suspension ring and chain
gold, enamel, lacquer
diamonds, onyx

175. _Vanity case_, circa 1925
rectangular, suspension chain
gold, enamel
diamonds

176. _Desk clock with easel_, circa 1920
square concave onyx plaque
gold, enamel
diamonds

177. _Desk clock with easel_, circa 1920
onyx hoop
gold, enamel
diamonds

178. _Desk clock with easel_, 1919
square concave agate plaque
gold, enamel
diamonds, sapphires

179. _Desk clock with easel_, circa 1920
square concave agate plaque
gold, enamel
diamonds, rubies

180. _Watch pendant_, 1920
gold, enamel
diamonds, onyx

181. _Watch pendant_, 1922
gold, enamel
onyx hoop, diamonds

182. _Fob watch_, 1923
gold, platinum, enamel
carved emeralds, diamonds
ILLUSTRATION XXVII

183. _Lady's bracelet watch_, 1920
platinum, gold
diamonds, onyx

184. _Lady's bracelet watch_, 1921
platinum
diamonds, pearls, onyx

185. _Watch clip_, circa 1920
in form of a miniature clock
platinum
diamonds

186. _Watch ring_, circa 1920
platinum
diamonds, sapphire

187. _Lady's wrist watch "Tortue"_, circa 1920
gold

188. _Pocket watch_, 1921
gold
sapphires

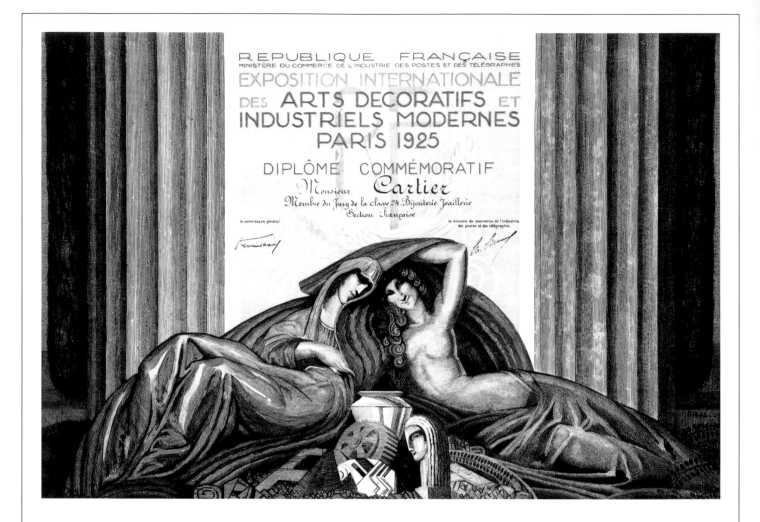

Louis Cartier was elected a member of the jury for jewellery of the French section at the 1925 International Exhibition which gave its name to the period of the early 20th century art.
Cartier's Museum Collection shows many convincing examples of the Art-Deco style well before the outbreak of World War I.

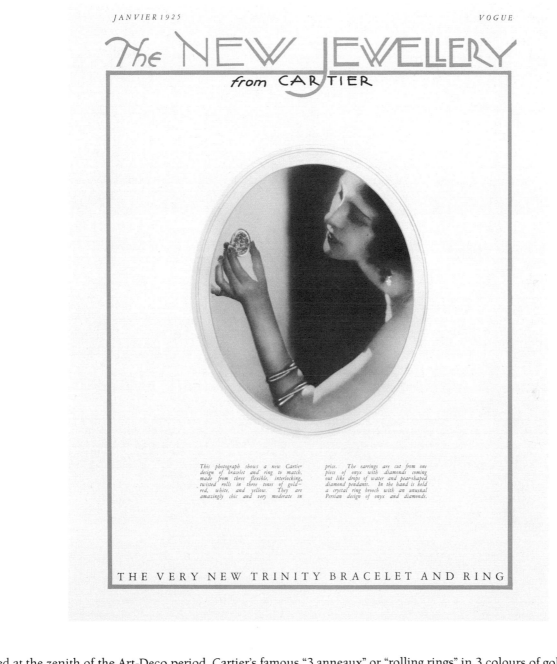

Created at the zenith of the Art-Deco period, Cartier's famous "3 anneaux" or "rolling rings" in 3 colours of gold have lost none of their attraction up to the present day.

XXVIII

XXIX

XXX

189. _Jabot pin_, 1923
in form of a closed Buddhist umbrella
platinum
diamonds, pearls, coral, onyx
ILLUSTRATION XXVIII

190. _Brooch_, 1924
platinum, rock-crystal
sapphire, diamonds, pearls, onyx
ILLUSTRATION XXX

191. _Brooch_, 1925
in form of a stylised Greek fruit cup
platinum, onyx
emerald, rubies, diamonds
Provenance: Mrs. W. K. Vanderbilt
ILLUSTRATION XXIX

192. _Brooch_, 1927
in form of a stylised Japanese flower basket
platinum, lapis-lazuli
rubies, diamonds, onyx

193. _Ring_, 1925
platinum
sapphire, diamonds

194. _Bracelet_, 1925
platinum
diamonds, coral, onyx

195. _Bracelet_, 1926
platinum
diamonds

196. _Perfume flask_, 1924
gold, enamel
rock-crystal, coral, pearl

197. _Perfume flask_, 1926
gold, enamel
Chinese carved jade, lapis-lazuli, sapphires

198. _Vanity case_, circa 1925
gold, enamel
jade, sapphires, diamonds
rock-crystal suspension hoop

199. _Vanity case_, circa 1926
gold, enamel
jade, sapphires, diamonds
onyx suspension hoop

200. _Vanity case_, circa 1925
gold, lacquer
diamonds, rubies, sapphires

201. _Vanity case_, 1927
gold, enamel, ivory
sapphires, emeralds, diamonds

202. _Mantle clock_, 1925
in fom of a Buddhist gong
gold, enamel
nephrite, lapis-lazuli, jade,
mother-of-pearl

203. _Desk clock with easel_, circa 1925
square concave agate plaque
gold, platinum
lapis-lazuli, diamonds, mother-of-pearl

204. _Desk clock with easel_, 1926
square concave jade plaque
gold, enamel
diamonds, mother-of-pearl

205. _Fob watch brooch_, 1923
gold, enamel, onyx
diamonds, coral

206. _Fob watch brooch_, 1926
gold, enamel, onyx
diamonds, rubies

207. _Lady's bracelet watch_, circa 1925
platinum
diamonds

208. _Lady's bracelet watch_, circa 1925
platinum
diamonds

209. _Lady's bracelet watch_, 1925
platinum, enamel
deployant gold and enamel buckle
Provenance: Jean-Charles Worth

210. _Lady's bracelet watch_, circa 1927
platinum
diamonds
deployant gold and enamel buckle

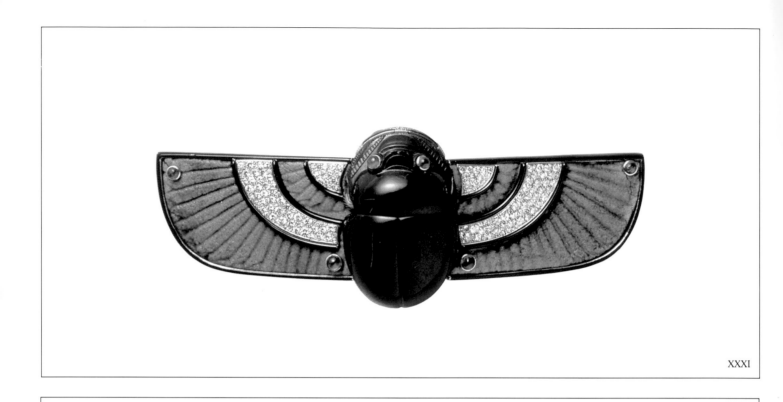

XXXI

XXXII

211. *Mantle clock, 1908*
in form of an Egyptian obelisk
green-brown spar, gold, enamel

212. *Necklace pendant, 1913*
in form of papyrus vase in temple gate
platinum
diamonds, onyx

213. *Brooch, 1924*
in form of an open-winged scarab
gold
ancient Egyptian earthenware, quartz
emeralds, diamonds
ILLUSTRATION XXXI

214. *Vanity case, 1928*
gold, enamel
diamonds
Provenance: Princess Amaryt of Kapurthala

215. *Desk clock, 1941*
gold, mother-of-pearl
antique Egyptian bas-relief, topaz, diamonds
Provenance: Mr. M. Solvay

216. *Cigarette case, 1920*
jade, gold, enamel
Persian miniature, diamonds, sapphires

217. *Vanity case with chain and ring, 1920*
gold, enamel
diamonds, onyx
Provenance: V. Astor

218. *Vanity case, 1924*
gold, enamel, mother-of-pearl, turquoise
pearls, emeralds, diamonds
ILLUSTRATION XXXII

219. *Vanity case, circa 1930*
gold, enamel
diamonds, onyx

220. *Vanity case, 1932*
gold, enamel
diamonds
Provenance: Duc d'Albe

221. *Powder compact with lipstick holder, 1924*
gold, enamel
diamonds

222. *Vanity case, circa 1925*
gold, enamel
diamonds

223. *Cigarette case, circa 1927*
gold, enamel
diamonds, rubies

224. *Cigarette case, circa 1928*
gold, enamel
diamonds

225. *Cigarette case, 1928*
silver, lacquer, gold, enamel
diamonds, onyx

226. *Cigarette case, 1929*
gold, enamel, agate
diamonds, emerald, rubies, sapphire

227. *Pocket lighter, 1928*
gold, enamel
diamonds

228. *Pocket lighter, circa 1928*
gold, enamel
diamonds

229. *Desk clock with easel, 1920*
gold, enamel, onyx
diamonds

230. *Miniature desk clock, 1925*
gold, enamel
diamonds, nephrite

231. *Fob watch brooch, 1925*
in form of a snaffle
platinum, gold, enamel
diamonds, coral, onyx

232. *Bangle, 1935*
gold

233. *Arm ornament*, 1922
platinum
diamonds
Provenance: Sir D. Bomanji
ILLUSTRATION XXXIII

234. *Jabot pin*, 1924
in form of a fibula
platinum
emeralds, diamonds

235. *Jabot pin*, 1923
in form of two palm leaves
platinum
emeralds, diamonds, onyx

236. *Brooch*, 1928
in form of a palm leaf
platinum
diamonds

237. *Turban pin "Turah"*, 1938
gold
rubies, diamonds, turquoises
pearls, sapphires, emeralds

238. *Desk clock*, 1928
rectangular
gold, enamel
onyx, jade

239. *Presentation cigarette box*, circa 1935
gold, enamel
interior inscription to the Shah Jahan

240. *Perfume flask*, circa 1925
carved emerald

Even though all creations at Cartier's remained usually anonymous, the archives give proof of an outstanding designer, who joined the company in 1909 and whose close cooperation with Louis Cartier lasted for twenty years: Charles Jacqueau.

His many sketch-books ("cahiers d'idées") adopt ideas from the "Gazette du bon ton", from visits to exhibitions and museums mainly the Louvre: the papyrus from Egypt (see 212), the central medallions of Persian carpets (see 218 ill. XXXII), the lotus in Indian miniatures (see 233 ill. XXXIII) and Far Eastern lacquer work (see chowcase XI). The greatest impression yet came from Diaghilev's "Ballets Russes" and his dancers, Vaslav Nijinsky, Karsavina, Ida Rubinstein, Anna Pavlova... dressed in Oriental, colourful costumes and with geometrically designed sceneries by Leon Bakst: Rimsky-Korsakov's "Schéhérazade". The impact of the "Ballets Russes" confirmed Louis Cartier's awareness of colours used since early 1900: red with black, purple with green, sapphires with emeralds or amethysts with sapphires, replacing the still fashionable pastel shades.

(SHOWCASE 12)

241. *Mantle clock*, 1926
in form of a Chinese gong-gate and "Fu" dogs
platinum, gold, silver, enamel
rock-crystal, mother-of-pearl, lapis-lazuli
ebony, diamonds, emeralds, rubies, sapphires
coral, onyx

242. *Desk clock*, "screen", 1922
platinum, gold, enamel
jade, onyx, coral
diamonds

243. *Desk clock*, "screen", circa 1926
platinum, gold, enamel
mother-of-pearl, onyx, coral
diamonds

244. *Calendar desk clock with easel*, 1910
four subsidiary dials
gold, silver, enamel
diamonds

245. *Calendar desk clock with easel*, 1910
four subsidiary dials
gold, silver, enamel
diamonds
Provenance: E. Mallet

246. *Gentleman's "hunter" wrist watch*, 1926
gold, enamel

247. *Gentleman's "Taxi" wrist watch*, 1928
two apertures: hours, minutes
gold
Provenance: Maharajah of Patiala

248. *Gentleman's wrist watch*, circa 1930
platinum

249. *"Taxi" pocket watch*, circa 1912
platinum

250. *"Skeleton" pocket watch*, circa 1929
gold, enamel
rock-crystal

251. *Mystery pocket watch*, circa 1931
platinum, enamel
rock-crystal

252. *Mystery pocket watch*, 1931
platinum, enamel
rock-crystal

253. *Coin watch*, 1930
$ 20 Liberty 1924 coin

(SHOWCASE 13)

254. *Mantle clock*, 1925
in form of two Chinese carps
platinum, gold, enamel
jade, rock-crystal, obsidian, mother-of-pearl
coral, diamonds
ILLUSTRATION XXXIV

255. *Desk clock with easel*, circa 1913
gold, enamel, agate
diamonds

256. *Desk clock with easel "chronoscope"*, 1913
gold, enamel, rock-crystal
diamonds

257. *Desk clock with easel*, 1919
gold, enamel, onyx
diamonds

258. *Desk clock with easel*, 1919
gold, enamel, onyx
diamonds

259. *Desk clock with easel "chronoscope"*, 1920
gold, enamel
Chinese lacquer, diamonds
inscription on reverse

260. *Miniature table clock*, 1928
in form of a triptych
gold, enamel
diamonds, onyx

261. *Miniature table clock*, circa 1929
in form of a triptych
gold, enamel, sapphires

XXXV

XXXVI

XXXVII

XXXVIII

(SHOWCASE 13   cont'd)

262. *Repeating pocket watch*, circa 1915
   gold
   ILLUSTRATION XXXV

263. *Repeating calendar pocket watch*, circa 1925
   gold
   ILLUSTRATION XXXVI

264. *Chronograph wrist watch*, "tonneau", 1925
   gold, enamel
   Provenance: Edsel Ford
   ILLUSTRATION XXXVII

265. *Precision wrist watch*, 1962
   four subsidiary dials
   gold
   ILLUSTRATION XXXVIII

(SHOWCASE 14)

266. *Mantle clock*, 1927
   in form of an agate sculpture of two birds
   amidst foliage supporting faceted topaz case,
   platinum, gold, enamel, lapis-lazuli
   diamonds

267. *Desk clock*, "dice", circa 1930
   barometer, thermometer, calendar, compass
   nephrite, gold, mother-of-pearl, marble
   sapphires

268. *Miniature travelling clock*, "Kodak", 1929
   gold, enamel
   sapphires

269. *Miniature travelling clock*, "eclipse", circa 1929
   gold, enamel

270. *Miniature travelling clock*, "Kodak", 1929
   gold, enamel
   sapphires
   Provenance: M. Pickford-Douglas Fairbanks

271. *Miniature prism clock*, 1952
   gold, rock-crystal
   Provenance: Prince Ali Khan

272. *Wrist watch*, circa 1920
   platinum
   Provenance: Count Marzotto

273. *Paperweight-watch*, circa 1939
   in form of a seated rock-crystal buddha
   gold, enamel

274. *Mantle clock*, 1970
   in form of a sculpture
   gold, silver, aquamarine
   lapis-lazuli, mother-of-pearl, turquoise
   diamonds

275. *Lady's wrist watch*, 1983
   in form of a gold turban
   diamonds
   prize for Paris-Algiers-Dakar Rally

276. *Gentleman's wrist watch*, 1985
   in form of a gold turban
   sapphire
   prize for Paris-Algiers-Dakar Rally

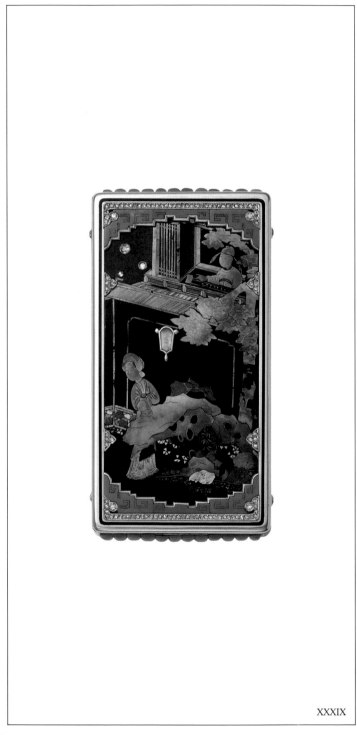

277. _Brooch_, circa 1920
in form of a buddha
gold, chrysoprase
diamonds, rubies, onyx

278. _Necklace pendant_, 1922
in form of a tassel
platinum, enamel
pearls, onyx, coral
diamonds

279. _Brooch_, 1928
in form of a Japanese flower vase
platinum, gold, enamel
lapis-lazuli, coral
diamonds, emeralds

280. _Desk clock_, 1925
gold, silver
Chinese lacquer, nephrite

281. _Mantle clock_, 1926
gold, enamel
jade, onyx, mother-of-pearl, agate
coral
diamonds

282. _Desk clock_, 1928
gold, silver, lacquer
Chinese lacquer, mother-of-pearl
Provenance: Mrs. de la Fressange

283. _Desk clock with easel_, circa 1929
gold, enamel, nephrite
Chinese lacquer, coral
diamonds

284. _Desk clock with easel_, 1929
gold, nephrite
Chinese lacquer, Kingfisher feathers
sapphires
Provenance: G. Munn

285. _Desk clock with easel_, 1929
gold, enamel
mother-of-pearl, Chinese lacquer
diamonds, coral

286. _Desk clock with easel_, 1929
gold, enamel, rock-crystal
Chinese lacquer
diamonds, sapphires
Provenance: Mrs. Warren Morgan

287. _Repeating desk clock_, circa 1930
gold, enamel
Chinese lacquer, mother-of-pearl
jade, onyx, diamonds

288. _Desk clock_, circa 1930
gold, enamel
Chinese lacquer, mother-of-pearl
jade, onyx, diamonds

289. _Powder box_, 1924
round
gold, white onyx
Chinese lacquer, ivory, ebonite

290. _Presentation cigarette case_, 1925
gold, enamel, nephrite
Chinese lacquer, coral, jade
diamonds, rubies
Provenance: Mr. F. Nelson-Morris

291. _Presentation cigarette case_, 1927
in form of a buddhist temple
gold, silver, enamel
antique Chinese porcelain plaque (19th century)
porcelain plaques, mother-of-pearl, ebonite

292. _Vanity case_, 1924
gold, enamel
jade, onyx
diamonds, emeralds

293. _Vanity case_, 1925
gold, enamel
Chinese lacquer
diamonds, sapphires, emeralds

294. _Vanity case_, 1926
gold, enamel
Chinese lacquer, mother-of-pearl
diamonds, coral
ILLUSTRATION XXXIX

295. _Vanity case_, 1926
platinum, gold, enamel
diamonds, Chinese pierced cornelian plaques

296. _Vanity case_, 1927
gold, enamel
diamonds

297. _Vanity case_, 1927
Chinese peonies and calices
platinum, gold, enamel
coral, topaz, moonstone
diamonds, sapphires, emeralds
ILLUSTRATION XL

298. _Vanity case_, 1928
gold, enamel
Chinese engraved jade (19th century)
mother-of-pearl, coral
diamonds

299. _Vanity case_, 1930
gold, enamel
diamonds

300. _Powder compact_, 1928
gold, enamel
Chinese lacquer, diamonds
Provenance: Duchess of Talleyrand

301. _Powder compact_, 1929
gold, enamel
mother-of-pearl and lacquer medallion signed
by Makowsky, diamonds, rubies
Provenance: Mrs. S. Soulas

302. _Cigarette case_, 1930
platinum, gold, enamel
Chinese lacquer
diamonds, rubies
(interior tortoiseshell)
Provenance: Mrs. F. Coty

303. _Ink-well_, 1926
in form of a miniature vase
gold, lacquer
Chinese lacquer panels
Provenance: Baron James A. de Rothschild

304. _Ink-well_, circa 1927
in form of a table bell push button
Chinese earthenware (19th century)
gold, lapis-lazuli
Provenance: Countess Mona Bismarck

305. _Ink-well_, circa 1927
in form of a tea-caddy
gold, enamel
Chinese lacquer (19th century)
ebonite
Provenance: Countess Mona Bismarck

306. _Paper-weight_, circa 1927
with Chinese ivory "Fu" dog (19th century)
gold, enamel, nephrite
sapphires, semi-precious stones

Cartier's delivery automobile in New York circa 1910

Cartier's workshop in rue Bachaumont circa 1930

307. *Car panel with St. Christopher*, circa 1906
gold, silver, enamel
sapphires

308. *Perfume flask*, 1927
rock-crystal
gold, enamel
topaz
"La Croisière Noire, 1925"

309. *Beauty case*, circa 1920
blue leather
silver accessories
Provenance: Mary Goodwell

310. *Beauty case*, circa 1928
brown crocodile leather
comprising complete beauty set

311. *Thermos vacuum flask*, circa 1920
one out of three
silver, pyrex

312. *Evening bag*, 1920
black satin
silver, enamel, onyx
diamond, pearl

313. *Evening bag*, 1928
antique brocade
clasp: ivory, gold, enamel, ebonite
diamond

314. *Handbag*, circa 1928
antique brocade
platinum, gold, enamel
onyx, diamonds, emeralds

315. *Desk clock*, circa 1925
agate, gold, enamel
rubies

316. *Desk clock*, 1927
rose quartz, gold, enamel
lapis-lazuli
diamonds

317. *Desk clock*, 1929
nephrite, gold, enamel
rock-crystal, rubies, turquoises

318. *Desk clock*, circa 1925
agate, gold, enamel, onyx

319. *Miniature travelling watch*, 1929
gold, enamel
diamonds, sapphires

320. *Miniature travelling watch*, "eclipse" 1929
gold, enamel
sapphires

321. *Repeating pocket watch*, circa 1930
gold
subsidiary second dial

322. *Pocket watch*, circa 1930
gold, enamel
onyx

323. *Watch-brooch*, circa 1935
tortoiseshell, gold

324. *Watch-brooch*, "golf", circa 1938
gold

325. *Cigarette case*, 1938
three colour gold
sapphire

326. *Cigarette shaft case with lighter*, 1939
gold

327. *Lipstick holder with watch*, circa 1947
gold
ruby

Queen Alexandra wearing her diamond "résille" necklace of 141.64 cts commissioned in 1904.
From a painting by François Flamand. Buckingham Palace. By gracious permission of Her Majesty The Queen Elizabeth II.

ROYAL WARRANTS

1904 King Edward VII
1904 King Alfonso XIII of Spain
1905 King Carlos of Portugal
1907 King of Siam
1907 Tsar Nicolas II of Russia
1909 King George I of Greece
1913 King Peter of Serbia
1914 Duke of Orleans
1919 King Albert I of Belgium
1920 King Victor Emmanuel III of Italy
1920 Prince Albert of Monaco
1921 Prince of Wales
1928 Queen Mary of Rumania
1929 King Fuad of Egypt
1939 King Zog I of Albania

XLI

XLII

XLIII

328. _Brooch, circa 1925_
in form of a ribbon-knot
white gold
diamonds, jet

329. _Brooch, circa 1925_
platinum, enamel
rock-crystal, diamonds

330. _Brooch, circa 1925_
platinum, enamel
diamonds

331. _Bracelet, 1926_
platinum
diamonds
Provenance: Hippolyte Worms

332. _Perfume flask, circa 1930_
nephrite, gold, enamel
rubies, onyx
ILLUSTRATION XLII

333. _Cigarette holder, circa 1925_
platinum
jade, onyx, diamonds

334. _Folding lorgnette pendant, circa 1926_
platinum, rock-crystal
diamonds

335. _Belt buckle, 1927_
platinum, gold, enamel
rock-crystal, diamonds
Provenance: Lady Martin Davis

336. _Powder compact and lipstick holder, 1924_
gold, enamel
diamonds
Provenance: Baron Roger

337. _Cigarette case, 1925_
gold, enamel
diamonds
Provenance: Banque Commerciale d'Orient

338. _Powder compact, circa 1925_
agate, platinum
jade, diamonds, onyx

339. _Podwer compact and lipstick holder, 1927_
gold, enamel
jade, sapphires
Provenance: Mrs. C. H. Sherill
ILLUSTRATION XLIII

340. _Desk clock, circa 1926_
arch-shaped nephrite plaque
gold, enamel
Kingfisher feathers, diamonds

341. _Desk clock, 1928_
arch-shaped nephrite plaque
gold, enamel
Kingfisher feathers
diamonds, rubies
ILLUSTRATION XLI

342. _Repeating desk clock, circa 1925_
platinum, gold, enamel, lacquer
Kingfisher feathers, onyx
diamonds

343. _Desk clock with easel, circa 1926_
gold, enamel
Chinese lacquer, mother-of-pearl
diamonds, turquoises

344. _Fob watch-brooch, 1925_
gold, enamel
white coral, diamonds

345. _Dress lapel watch, 1925_
platinum, onyx
diamonds

346. _Lady's bracelet watch, 1925_
platinum
diamonds, pavé-set pearl bracelet
Provenance: Maharajah of Cashmere

347. _Lady's bracelet watch, 1926_
platinum
diamonds, gold and enamel deployant buckle
Provenance: Duchess of Marlborough

XLV

XLIV

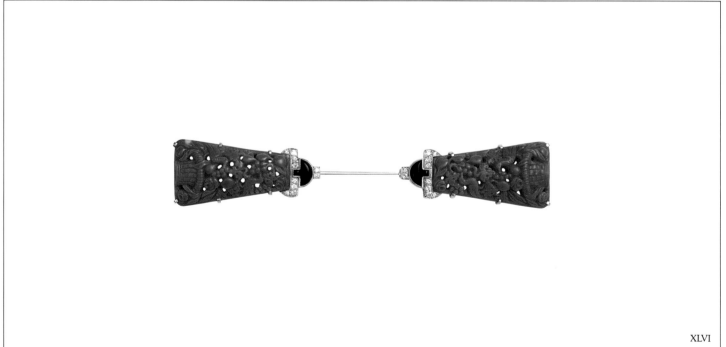

XLVI

348. _Brooch, circa 1927_
in form of a stylised temple of love
platinum
diamonds
ILLUSTRATION XLIV

349. _Brooch, circa 1928_
in form of a fountain with birds
platinum, enamel
diamonds

350. _Jabot-pin, 1928_
in form of a fibula
platinum
sapphires, diamonds
Provenance: H.M. The Queen of Serbia
ILLUSTRATION XLV

351. _Jabot-pin, circa 1930_
platinum
two engraved coral plaques
onyx, diamonds
ILLUSTRATION XLVI

352. _Link bracelet, 1930_
platinum, rock-crystal lining
diamonds
Provenance: Baron Robert de Rothschild

353. _Cigarette holder, 1928_
platinum, jet, coral
diamonds, emeralds

354. _Cigarette holder, circa 1925_
platinum, coral, lapis-lazuli
diamonds, emeralds

355. _Pocket lighter, circa 1928_
gold, enamel
coral

356. _Pair of perfume flasks and support, 1928_
gold
rock-crystal, lapis-lazuli, coral, onyx
rubies
Provenance: Sir Robert Adby

357. _Belt-buckle, 1928_
gold
engraved jade, turquoises, sapphires
Provenance: R. Stuyvesand

358. _Twin powder compact, 1928_
gold, enamel
pierced jade plaque, rubies

359. _Vanity case, 1929_
gold, enamel
engraved jade, diamonds

360. _Powder compact, 1929_
gold
turquoise, lapis-lazuli
Provenance: Duchess of Talleyrand

361. _Vanity case, 1929_
gold, enamel, lacquer
lapis-lazuli,
diamonds, rubies, emeralds
Provenance: C.I. Weil

362. _Vanity case, 1929_
gold, enamel

363. _Desk clock with easel, 1928_
arch-shaped rutile rock-crystal plaque
gold, enamel
rubies

364. _Desk clock with easel, 1928_
arch-shaped agate plaque
gold, enamel
engraved jade, emeralds

365. _Desk clock with easel, 1929_
square (incurved) agate plaque
gold, enamel
engraved jade, mother-of-pearl

366. _Desk clock with easel, circa 1929_
arch-shaped rock-crystal plaque
platinum, gold, enamel
diamonds, rubies, jade

367. _Desk clock with easel, 1920_
octagonal rock-crystal plaque
gold, silver, enamel
diamonds
Provenance: L. Hirsch

368. _Lady's bracelet watch, circa 1927_
platinum
pavé-set diamond hunter case and
bracelet

369. _Lady's bracelet watch, circa 1925_
platinum
diamond bezel and bracelet

370. _Lady's miniature bracelet watch, circa 1928_
platinum case and link bracelet

371. _Lady's wrist watch "tonneau", circa 1929_
curved gold case and deployant buckle
sapphire

Showcase at the 1925 "Art-Déco" Exhibition in Paris.
"Bérénice"-tiara, ear-pendants, "épaulette" and brooch with engraved emeralds, pearls and diamonds.

EXPOSITION FRANÇAISE AU CAIRE 1929

Groupe N

DIPLÔME
DE
HORS CONCOURS
MEMBRE DU JURY

Classe 95

DÉCERNÉ À Société anonyme CARTIER, à Paris.

LE CONSEILLER D'ÉTAT
DÉLÉGUÉ DU GOUVERNEMENT

LE PRÉSIDENT DU COMITÉ
FRANÇAIS DES EXPOSITIONS

LE PRÉSIDENT DU COMITÉ
D'ORGANISATION DE L'EXPOSITION

SÉNATEUR ANCIEN MINISTRE

Many events linked England and France to Egypt and influenced decorative arts and jewellery over decades: Napoleon I Egyptian campaign, 1798 - Champollion's deciphering of the hieroglyphs, 1822 - obelisk offered to Louis XVIII, Place de la Condorde, 1831 - opening of Suez Canal built by Lesseps, 1831 - première of Verdi's Aïda, 1871 - discovery by Ayrton of royal tomb, Thebes, 1908 - Franco-Egyptian exhibition, Louvre, 1911 - discovery by Borchardt of Nefertiti's head, 1912 - discovery by Carter/Carnarvon of Tutankhamun's tomb, 1922.

The fascination of these events inspired Cartier to create the "Egyptian" jewels reported in "London Illustrated News", 1924. (see also 213, ill. XXXI and 215).

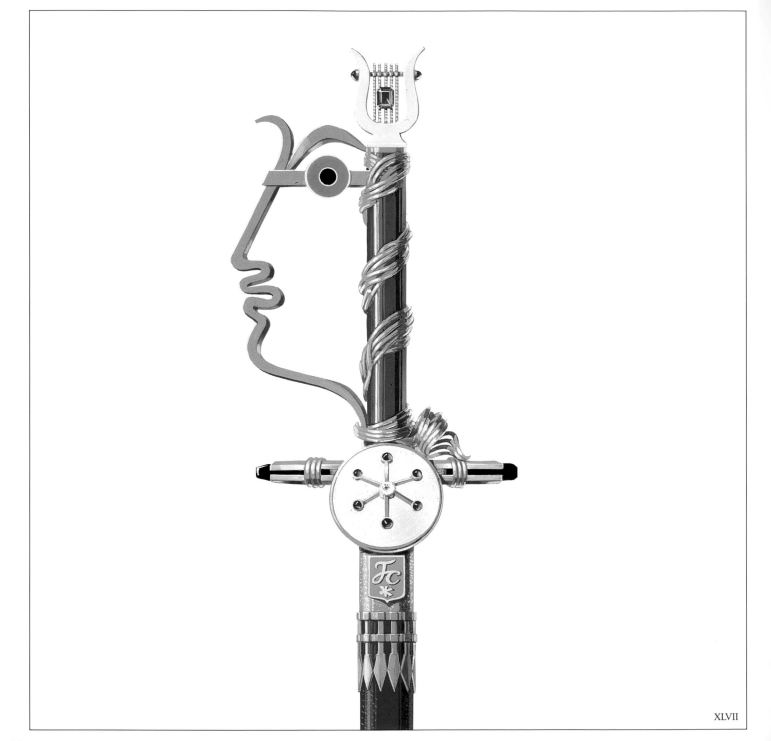

372. *Maltese cross pendant, 1935 and 1949*
platinum, gold
various precious and semi-precious stones,
pearls

373. *Vanity case, 1936*
gold
jade, colour stones
Provenance: Lady Fellowes

374. *Repeating desk clock, 1930*
gold, silver
jasper, lapis-lazuli
diamonds

375. *Repeating musical desk clock, circa 1955*
gold, silver, enamel
melody of "la vie en rose"

376. *Presentation cigarette box, circa 1930*
gold, enamel, agate plaques
diamonds, jade

377. *Presentation cigarette casket, 1935*
gold, enamel
nephrite, jade

378. *Letter-opener, 1943*
platinum, gold, silver, lacquer
coral chimera, diamond

379. *Academician Sword, 1955*
platinum, gold, enamel
diamond, emerald, rubies
Provenance: Jean Cocteau
ILLUSTRATION XLVII (design)

*Cartier Jewellers
thank
Edouard Dhermit
for the kind loan of
his father's
Academician's Sword*

(SEE PAGE 89)

JEAN COCTEAU'S ACADEMICIAN'S SWORD

Over the years Cocteau had been much inspired by Orpheus, the mythological poet and musician. This was reflected in his work:

In poetry ("Orphée" 1927) and on the screen ("La Machine Infernale" and "Le Testament d'Orphée"). The sword portrays the profile of Orpheus surmounted by his lyre, which is decorated with an emerald of 2.84 cts given by Coco Chanel.

The hilt of the sheath entwined with a ribbon symbolises the theatre, especially tragedy.

The horizontal chalk pencil stays for the graphic art (posters for "Le Spectre de la Rose").

The tiny bronze hand grasping the ivory ball is reminiscent of the snow covered stone in "Les Enfants Terribles".

The lances remind of the grille of the Palais-Royal where he lived as Colette's neighbour.

The sword is signed with the initials "JC" and a small six-pointed star below, as in all his writings. Above, this symbol is repeated in a larger ornament on ivory with a cabochon ruby at each of the six points and a central diamond given by Francine Weisweiller.

Cocteau's own design and Cartier's skill resulted in a particularly beautiful and very original sword:
The poet was very much moved looking at the interpretation of his design completed in simple beauty. He said "you will place it by my side on my death bed, I am proud that it should be the most beautiful of them all".

XLVIII

XLIX

L

380. *Lady's belt/sautoir*, circa 1930
gold
jade, rubies

381. *Brooch*, 1937
in form of a hand holding a rose
platinum, gold, silver, lacquer
diamonds
Provenance: J.L. Wilson

382. *Flower brooch*, circa 1939
gold, platinum, onyx
carved emerald, diamonds, rubies

383. *Flower brooch*, 1940
platinum, gold
emeralds, rubies, diamonds

384. *Desk clock with easel*, 1929
square concave rock-crystal plaque
gold, silver, enamel
sapphires, turquoises

385. *Desk clock with easel*, 1930
arch-shaped rock-crystal plaque,
gold, enamel
jade

386. *Watch pendant*, circa 1920
platinum
diamonds, onyx
ILLUSTRATION XLVIII

387. *Evening handbag*, circa 1925
black satin
platinum frame
diamonds, onyx

388. *"Panther" vanity case*, 1928
white gold, platinum, lacquer
diamonds, emeralds, rubies
Provenance: Leopold Marx
ILLUSTRATION XLIX

389. *Bracelet*, 1930
platinum
reeded coral beads, diamonds,
onyx
ILLUSTRATION L

390. *Clip Brooch*, 1949
in form of a panther on sapphire globe
platinum, white gold
diamonds, sapphires
Provenance: Duchess of Windsor
ILLUSTRATION LI

391. *Tiger-lorgnette*, 1954
gold, enamel
emerald eyes
Provenance: Duchess of Windsor
ILLUSTRATION LII

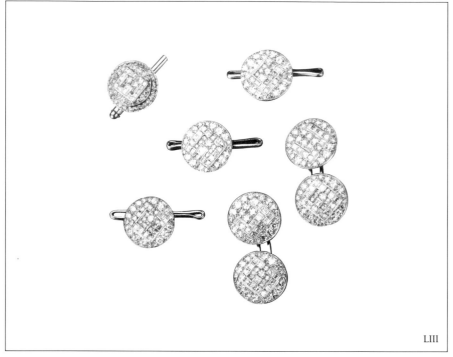

LIII

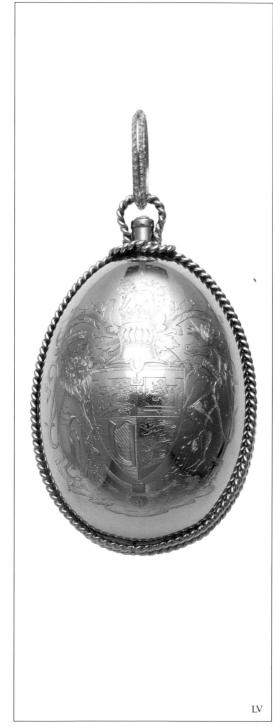

LV

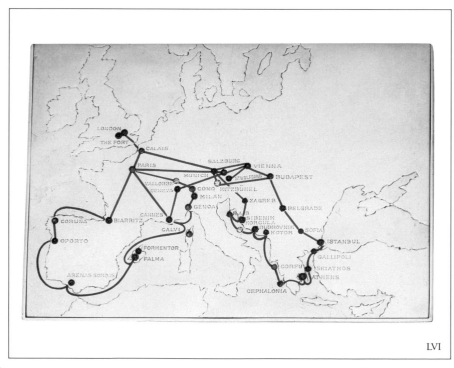

LVI

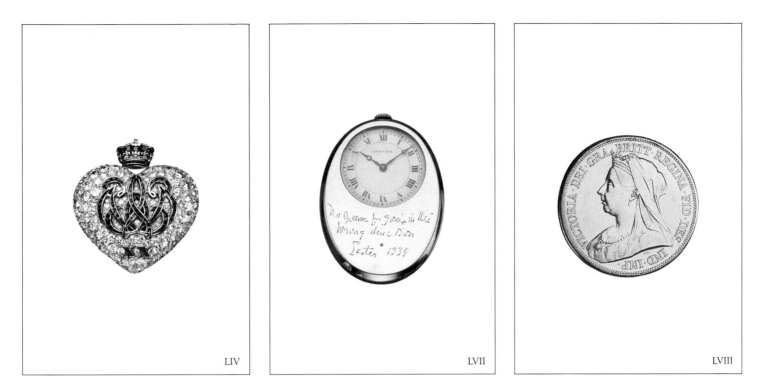

LIV

LVII

LVIII

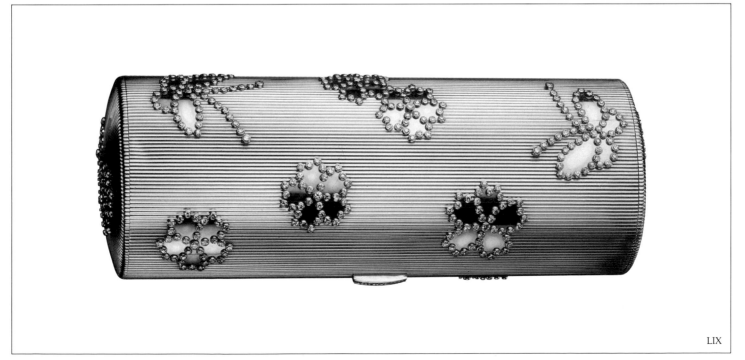

LIX

LX

LXI

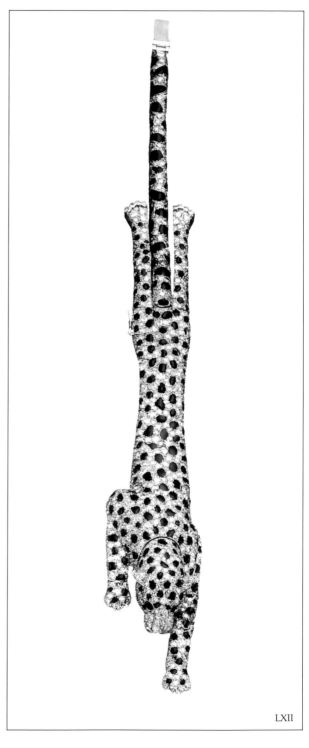

LXII

392. _Dress Suite_, 1935
diamonds
comprising: pair of cuff-links,
a stud, three buttons
Provenance: Duchess of Windsor
ILLUSTRATION LIII

393. _Heart Brooch_, 1957
platinum, gold
diamonds, rubies, emeralds
Provenance: Duchess of Windsor
ILLUSTRATION LIV

394. _Powder compact_, circa 1950
in form of an egg
gold, diamonds
Provenance: Duchess of Windsor
ILLUSTRATION LV

395. _Cigarette case_, 1935
gold
cabochon gems
Provenance: Duchess of Windsor
ILLUSTRATION LVI

396. _Pocket watch_, circa 1938
gold
Provenance: Duchess of Windsor
ILLUSTRATION LVII

397. _Coin watch_, circa 1848
£ 5 coin 1893
fritted leather pouch
Provenance: Duchess of Windsor
ILLUSTRATION LVIII

398. _Evening vanity case_, 1947
gold flat cylinder
diamonds
Provenance: Duchess of Windsor
ILLUSTRATION LIX

399. _Clip_, 1940
in form of a flamingo
platinum
diamonds, rubies, emeralds, sapphires
citrine
Provenance: Duchess of Windsor
ILLUSTRATION LX

400. _Charm bracelet_, circa 1935
platinum, diamonds
9 cross charms of precious and
semi-precious stones
Provenance: Duchess of Windsor
ILLUSTRATION LXI

401. _Panther bracelet_, 1952
platinum
diamonds, onyx, emeralds
Provenance: Duchess of Windsor
ILLUSTRATION LXII

By courtesy of Mr. Wafik Rida Said

The Duchess of Windsor wearing the brooch with a sculptured panther in platinum set with diamonds, sapphire dots and yellow sapphire eyes sitting on a round cabochon sapphire of 152.39 cts.

This jewel was bought back for Sfr. 1,540,000.– for the Cartier Museum from the Duchess of Windsor's estate auctioned by Sotheby's in Geneva in Spring 1987 and bequeathed to the "Institut Pasteur" in Paris for the cancer research.

Jeanne Toussaint (1887-1978) described by Sir Cecil Beaton as "a woman of small, bird-like stature" was appointed by the three Cartier brothers "Directrice à la Haute Joaillerie" in 1933. Not a designer herself, but endowed with a sixth sense of taste, the famous "goût Toussaint", she created in 1948 the panther brooch (see 390, illustration LI) which was commissioned by the Duchess of Windsor. Jeanne Toussaint, nicknamed "the panther" by her friends, inspired many successive and successful creations, promoting this elegant wild cat to be the secret symbol of Cartier.

402. *Pair of clips*, *1929*
platinum
diamonds, rubies, emeralds
ILLUSTRATION LXIII

403. *Bracelet*, *circa 1930*
in form of a fruit branch
platinum
diamonds, rubies, sapphires, emeralds
ILLUSTRATION LXIV

404. *Lady's bracelet watch*, *circa 1926*
platinum
diamonds, rubies

405. *Evening bag*, *1929*
blue reindeer
platinum, gold,
enamel
diamonds, rubies, emeralds

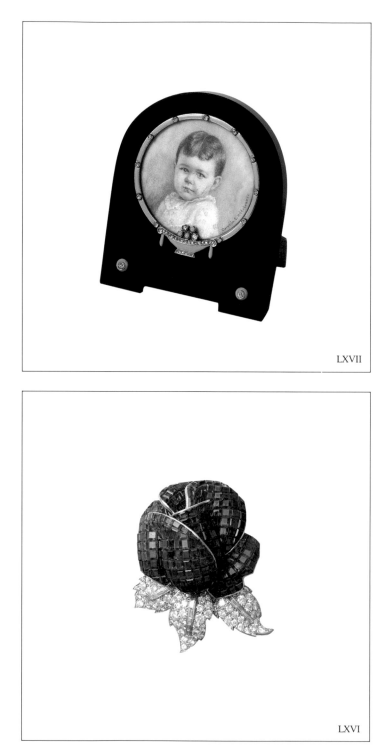

LXVII

LXVI

LXV

406. *Necklace and pendant*, 1933
     platinum
     diamonds, rubies, sapphires
     ILLUSTRATION LXV

407. *Clip*, 1960
     in form of a rose-blossom
     platinum
     invisibly set-sapphires
     diamonds
     ILLUSTRATION LXVI

408. *Desk clock with easel*, 1928
     rectangular onyx plaque
     gold
     diamonds, sapphires

409. *Desk clock with easel*, circa 1930
     square nephrite
     gold, metal

410. *Cigarette case and lighter*, circa 1930
     gold, enamel

411. *Desk frame*, circa 1927
     arch-shaped onyx plaque
     platinum, gold,
     enamel
     miniature signed by Cornelia E. Hildebrands
     diamonds, turquoises
     ILLUSTRATION LXVII

LXVIII

LXIX

412. *Brooch*, 1930
in form of a skier
platinum
diamonds, rubies

413. *Clip*, 1932
in form of a stylised spade
platinum
diamonds

414. *Pin*, 1937
in form of a flower
platinum
diamonds

415. *Ladybird brooch*, 1935
platinum, white gold, lacquer
coral, diamonds

416. *Ladybird brooch*, 1936
platinum, white gold, lacquer
coral, diamonds

417. *Ring*, 1933
platinum
coral, onyx, diamonds

418. *Bracelet*, 1931
detachable flower centre as brooch
platinum
diamonds

419. *Curb chain bracelet*, 1933
heavy platinum curb chain, enamel
carved sapphire
Provenance: H.M. The King of Yugoslavia

420. *Bracelet*, 1937
platinum, white gold
lapis-lazuli beads, diamonds, turquoises
ILLUSTRATION LXVIII

421. *Desk clock with easel*, 1930
arch-shaped onyx plaque
platinum, gold, enamel
mother-of-pearl, diamonds

422. *Desk clock with easel*, circa 1939
gold
onyx hoop, reeded coral beads,
agate, rock-crystal
diamonds, rubies

423. *Dress pocket watch*, 1930
platinum, gold, enamel
rock-crystal, onyx

424. *Dress pocket watch*, circa 1930
nephrite, gold, enamel

425. *Pocket watch*, circa 1930
onyx, gold

426. *Cigarette case, 1932
in form of an addressed envelope
gold, enamel
Provenance: Sir Winston Churchill
ILLUSTRATION LXIX

427. *Cigarette case*, 1934
gold
sapphires
Provenance: Prince Tikka Rajah of
Kapurthala

428. *Powder compact*, 1932
silver, lacquer
reeded coral beads, diamonds

429. *Desk lighter*, 1939
gold, silver, enamel
Chinese engraved jade flask
coral, diamonds

430. *Lady's wrist watch*, 1931
gold

431. *Lady's bangle watch*, circa 1938
gold

432. *Watch clip*, "mandoline", 1939
gold

433. *Watch ring*, 1938
gold
rubies

434. *Miniature bracelet watch*, 1932
platinum
Prince Tikka Rajah of Kapurthala

435. *Lady's bracelet watch*, 1937
platinum
diamonds

---

* Present given to his son Randolph on the occasion of his 21st birthday, engraved with Sir Winston Churchill's handwriting.

LXX

LXXI

LXXII

LXXIII

82

436. _Scarab brooch_, 1945
platinum, gold
lapis-lazuli, turquoises, diamonds

* 437. _Cigarette case_, 1945
gold
Provenance: Gouvernement Provisoire
de la République Française

438. _"Inseparables" bird brooch_, 1941
platinum, gold
sapphires, diamonds, emeralds
ILLUSTRATION LXXI

** 439. _"Bird out of the cage" brooch_, 1946
gold
coral, lapis, diamonds, sapphire
ILLUSTRATION LXX

440. _Flower brooch_, 1946
gold, platinum
diamonds

441. _Paradise bird clip_, 1949
gold
diamonds, sapphires, emeralds

442. _Spaniel brooch_, 1951
platinum
diamonds

443. _Dragon-fly brooch_, 1953
platinum, gold
diamonds, emeralds, rubies

444. _Rose brooch_, 1955
gold

445. _Eagle-head pin_, 1958
platinum, gold
onyx, pearl, ruby, diamonds
ILLUSTRATION LXXII

446. _Bird brooch_, 1960
platinum, white gold
ruby, diamonds, emerald
Provenance: Mrs. Morris Steiner
ILLUSTRATION LXXIII

* Engraved with the Cross of Lorraine and Charles de Gaulle's signature in handwriting.

There were very strong links between Cartier London and Général de Gaulle. When, after Dunkirk, the General first arrived in London, he and his family stayed at the Cartier director's and Madame Bellenger's house in Putney. Cartier's workshop, the English Art Work, producing intricate parts for aircrafts and cameras, was asked to create the Cross of Lorraine, which became the emblem worn with the uniform of the Free French Forces.

Cartier's board room was held at the disposal of General de Gaulle for meetings and also for preparing the statement he was to pronounce on the BBC on June 18, 1940.

** The "bird in the cage" was originally designed for a bracelet made for Yvonne Printemps.

As a brooch it became Cartier's secret symbol for the occupation. The jewelled secret was disclosed when after the liberation the same brooch showed the little bird singing at the open door of the cage.

Baguette

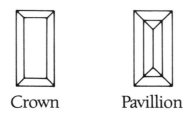

Crown   Pavillion

A FRENCH WORD MEANING "ROD". A STYLE OF STEP-CUTTING FOR SMALL, RECTANGULARLY-SHAPED GEMSTONES, PRINCIPALLY DIAMONDS.

"The Diamond Dictionary" Gemological Institute of America. Second Edition 1977

The invention of this bold cut is attributed to Louis Cartier in 1912. It found its application principally in the geometric designs of the Art-Deco jewellery in the late Twenties and again in the Fifties.

Design patents, utility models and patents

1909 folding buckle
1913 mystery clock
1926 handbag clasp
      brooch clip
      watch, face turned towards bracelet
1930 gold alloys
1933 invisible setting ("serti mystérieux")
      lipstick holder
      watch, to be worn on inside edge of wrist
1935 lipstick holder
1937 prism clock
1938 twin lipstick holder
1939 rotating cuff-links
1940 "forget-me-not" accessories' holder
1941 chronometric instrument with dial and digital reading
1942 (another) mystery clock
1945 skeleton waist watch
1946 clock showing time by projection
••••
••••

This selection of the many applications, registrations and patents granted prove Cartier's rich creativity in technical and aesthetical innovations conveyed to the art of jewellery.

The Grand Duchess Vladimir with the briolette diamond tiara by Cartier (1908) appearing through the opening of the Russian headdress, with, at its base, the 19th century Russian emerald necklace.

Barbara Hutton wearing the Cartier tiara (which transforms to a necklace) with the Russian emeralds of the necklace of the Grand Duchess Vladimir. At her finger, the Pasha of Egypt diamond. Originally an octagonal Indian diamond of 40 cts, at her request it was later recut by Cartier to a brilliant of 38.19 cts. The present owner had it recut to 36.22 cts: the biggest D-flawless brilliant according to the GIA records.

447. _Coconut tree clip_, 1957
     platinum, white gold
     Burma rubies, diamonds
     ILLUSTRATION LXXIV

448. _Pair of clips_, 1957
     platinum
     diamonds, sapphires
     Provenance: E. Loder

449. _Seastar brooch_, 1969
     platinum, gold
     emerald, rubies, diamonds

450. _Rose brooch_, circa 1972
     in form of two rose blossoms
     platinum, white gold
     coral, diamonds

451. _Bracelet_, 1955
     platinum
     reeded coral beads, coral, diamonds
     Provenance: Mrs. J. Donahue

452. _Bangle_, 1968
     platinum, gold
     coral, diamonds

453. _Ring_, 1956
     platinum, gold
     ruby beads, diamonds

454. _Lipstick holder_, 1948
     gold
     rubies, sapphires

455. _Lady's cigarette case_, 1949
     gold cylinder
     rubies

456. _Gentleman's bracelet watch_, "reverso", 1942
     gold case and link bracelet

457. _Lady's bracelet watch_, 1946
     gold case and link bracelet

458. _Gentleman's wrist watch_, 1947
     gold

459. _Lady's bracelet watch_, 1950
     square gold case, flexible gold baton link
     bracelet
     Provenance: Maharajah of Kapurthala

460. _Watch clip_, circa 1960
     gold
     coral, diamonds

461. _Cigarette case_, circa 1963
     gold, enamel
     lapis-lazuli, garnet
     Provenance: Wilding Collection
     (See also: British Museum)

CROQUIS

SEE 388 - ILL. L

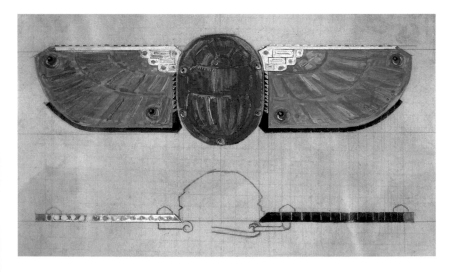

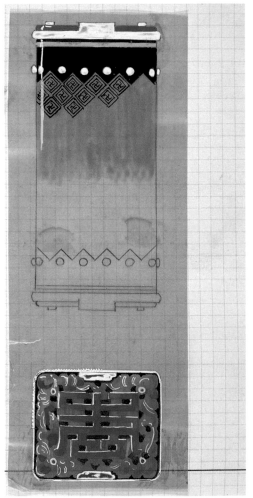

SEE 295

SEE 213 - ILL. XXXI

Marshals' Batons

1920   Maréchal Ferdinand Foch
1920   Maréchal Philippe Pétain
Now to be seen at the "Musée de l'Armée" in Paris

French Academicians' Swords

The "Académie Française" originated in a loose association of scholars, organized on a regular basis by Richelieu in 1634 to foster the French language. The great dictionary was the sole fruit of its labours but that was sufficient to spread its renown throughout France. Dissolved at the Revolution, it was reconstituted 1794 as a part of the "Institut de France", whose five sections survive to this day: the "Académie Française", the "Académie des Inscriptions et Belles Lettres", the "Académie des Sciences" and the "Académie des Sciences Morales et Politiques".

Since Napoleon's time, the 40 members wear a black ceremonial dress decorated with green olive branches. Later the dress regulation came to be supplemented with a sword, reflecting their work and significance and presented to the newly elected academicians by friends and admirers.

Between 1931 and now, Cartier received 26 commissions for these unique ornaments:

1931	Duc de Gramont	1954	Alfred Pose
1933	François Mauriac	1955	Jean Cocteau (see pages 64/65)
1936	Georges Duhamel	1956	Daniel Rops
1938	Jacques de Lacretelle	1957	Vladimir d'Ormesson
1938	James Hyde	1960	Jean Delay
1939	André Maurois	1963	Gaston Cordier
1945	Pasteur Valéry Radot	1964	Joseph Kessel
1946	Jules Romains	1967	Pierre-Henri Simon
1947	Henri Mondor	1967	Maurice Druon
1947	Maurice Genevoix	1971	Georges Izard
1947	Jacques Rueff	1975	Jean Hamburger
1953	Julien Cain	1986	Louis Pauwels
1954	Duc de Lévis-Mirepoix	1986	Jean-François Bach

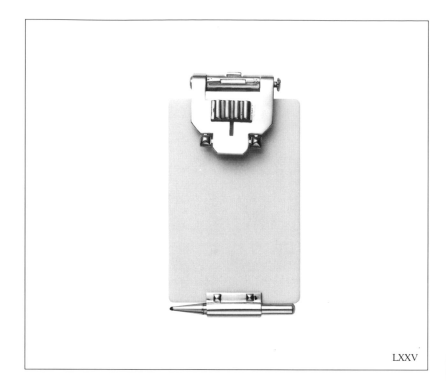

LXXV

LXXVI

LXXVII

462. *Centimeter cylinder*, circa 1906
gold, enamel
sapphires

463. *Perfume vaporizer flask*, 1912
gold, enamel
diamonds, pearls

464. *Desk frame with easel*, circa 1922
nephrite, platinum, gold, enamel
diamonds

465. *Writing pad support with pencil*, circa 1925
gold, ivory
ILLUSTRATION LXXV

466. *Bonbonnière*, 1926
agate cup and cover
gold, enamel
coral, onyx
Provenance: Mrs. Gay O'Brian
ILLUSTRATION LXXVII

467. *Mantle clock, "globe"*, circa 1926
gold, enamel
onyx, coral, ebonite

468. *Calendar desk clock/paper weight*, circa 1927
nephrite, gold, enamel
coral

469. *Comb and shaft*, 1928
antique brocade shaft
tortoiseshell comb
gold, enamel
emerald, diamonds
ILLUSTRATION LXXVI

470. *Pocket lighter*, 1929
gold, enamel

471. *Pocket cigar case and shaft*, 1929
gold, enamel

472. *Evening handbag*, circa 1929
black satin
gold, enamel
emeralds, diamonds

473. *Letter opener*, 1930
silver
lapis-lazuli

474. *Gold pencil*, circa 1930
inset with a watch
ILLUSTRATION LXXVIII

475. *Desk set*, circa 1930
agate, gilt metal, lacquer

476. *Lipstick holder with watch*, circa 1930
gold

477. *Powder compact*, 1930
platinum, silver, lacquer
coral, diamonds
Provenance: Mr. Besansoy de Wagner

478. *Combined ink-pen and pencil*, circa 1930
gold
shagreen shaft

479. *Match case*, circa 1930
gold, enamel

480. *Pocket lighter*, circa 1932
gold, silver, lacquer
coral

481. *Bonbonnière*, 1934
rock-crystal bowl
gold, lacquer, ebonite
coral
Provenance: Mrs. Kilvert

LXXVIII

LXXIX

LXXX

482. _Lipstick holder, 1935_
     silver, lacquer, platinum
     coral, diamond
     model created for Guerlain

483. _Bangle, 1935_
     gold, enamel

484. _Perpetual calendar coin, circa 1935_
     gold, enamel

485. _Pocket lighter, circa 1935_
     gold

486. _Hand mirror, 1940_
     gold, nephrite
     carnelian

487. _Cigarette case_, "Kodak", _1943_
     gold, enamel

488. _Pocket lighter, 1944_
     gadrooned gold

489. _Cigarette case, circa 1944_
     two colour gold, enamel

490. _Lipstick holder with watch, circa 1945_
     gold

491. _Pocket lighter, circa 1945_
     gold, oval sections
     diamonds

492. _Bracelet, 1945_
     in form of a double splice rope
     gold
     rubies, sapphires, diamonds

493. _Gold pencil, 1947_
     diamonds

494. _Watch locket, 1948_
     gold
     ILLUSTRATION LXXIX

495. _Ladybird pocket lighter, 1949_
     silver, lacquer
     coral, diamonds

496. _Powder compact, 1949_
     gold
     diamonds

497. _Pocket lighter, 1952_
     gold, silver

498. _Pocket lighter, 1956_
     gold

499. _Miniature clock, 1961_
     in form of a drum
     gold

500. _Gentleman's "Tank" wrist watch, 1970_
     gold, sapphire
     Provenance: President Edgar Faure
     ILLUSTRATION LXXX

FAMOUS DIAMONDS AT CARTIER'S

1907 "Star of the South", 15.46 cts, sold to Mrs. Evalyn McLean
1908 "Star of the East", 94.80 cts, sold to Mrs. Evalyn McLean
1910 Blue "Hope", 44.50 cts, sold to Mrs. Evalyn McLean
1911 "Blue Heart", 31.00 cts, sold to Mrs. Unzue
1911 Pear-shaped diamond, 43.00 cts, sold to Mrs. Rita Lydig
1931 "Queen of Holland", 136.25 cts, sold to the Maharajah of Nawanagar
1933 "Porter Rhodes", 56.50 cts, sold to Sir Ernest Oppenheimer
1933 "Nassak", 80.60 cts at Cartier London, recut in 1937 to 47.41 cts.
1936 "Cumberland", 32.82 cts, at Cartier Monte Carlo
1937 "Tigereye", 61.50 cts, sold to the Maharajah of Nawanagar
1937 "Jubilee", 245.35 cts, sold to Mr. P.-L. Weiller
1964 "Vega", 14.00 cts, sold by Cartier New York
1969 "Burton-Taylor-Cartier", 69.42 cts, sold to Mr. Richard Burton
1976 "Louis Cartier", 107.07 cts, sold to a European collector

• • • •
• • • •

FAMOUS NAMES AT CARTIER'S

Duchess of Devonshire   Anna Gould   Mistinguett
Caroline Otero   The Aga Khan   Queen of Spain   Churchill   Duc d'Orléans   Countess of Nieuwerkerke
Princesse de Polignac   Enrico Caruso   Jeanne Lanvin   Mrs. Solvay   Gaekwar of Baroda   Vicomtesse Astor
Coco Chanel   Maharajah of Patiala   de Rothschild   Princess Victoria
Duchess of Roxburghe   Jean Cocteau   Empress Eugénie   Princess Mathilde   Grand Duke Paul   Cornelius Vanderbilt
Queen Elizabeth of Belgium   Comtesse de Turenne   Dodge   Lady Cunard
Prince of Wales   Nizam of Hyderabad   Tsar Nicolas II of Russia   Lady Grey   Marquis of Anglesey
King George I of Greece   Barbara Hutton   Mrs. Unzue   Maharajah of Dhranghadra
Vicomtesse de Bonnemain   Maharajah of Jaipur   King of Sweden
Sultan of Zanzibar   Princesse de Wagram   Prince Pedro of Brazil   King Zog I of Albania   Eleonora Duse
Prince Albert de Monaco   Princesse George Radziwill   Grand Duchess Vladimir   King Peter of Serbia
King Albert I of Belgium   King Ferdinand of Rumania   Princesse Amédée de Broglie
Lillie Langry   Thyssen   Maria Félix   King of Siam   Duchess of Fitz-James   Countess Greffulhe
King Fuad of Egypt   Queen Sophie of Greece   Countess Warwick
Nellie Melba   Maharajah of Kapurthala   Maharajah of Patna   Maharajah of Nawanagar   Diaghilev
Prince Youssoupov   Countess Essex
Queen Mary of Rumania   Prince de Saxe-Cobourg   Lady Curzon of Keddleston   Prince Soltikov   J.P. Morgan
Maharajah of Indore   Duke of Westminster   Mrs. Walsh McLean
Duchess of Manchester   King Carlos of Portugal   Arthur Rubinstein   Queen Helen of Italy
Elizabeth Taylor   Queen Alexandra   Santos Dumont

H.M. The Queen Elizabeth II with H.R.H. Princess Anne, photographed in 1954 wearing the Williamson–Cartier diamond brooch. The pink brilliant of 23.52 cts cut from a rough stone of over 54 cts found in Mwadwi, Tanganyika (Tanzania) in 1947 was presented to Princess Elizabeth the same year as a wedding gift by the Canadian geologist Dr. John T. Williams.
In 1952, Cartier mounted this rare rose colour brilliant on a flower brooch (Edelweiss) set with 203 diamonds of various shapes of a total weight of 27.46 cts.

CARTIER FAMILY TREE

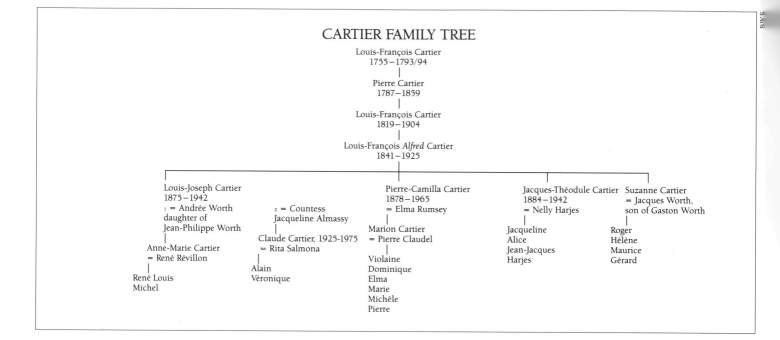

Louis-François Cartier
1755–1793/94

Pierre Cartier
1787–1859

Louis-François Cartier
1819–1904

Louis-François *Alfred* Cartier
1841–1925

Louis-Joseph Cartier
1875–1942
₁ = Andrée Worth
daughter of
Jean-Philippe Worth

₂ = Countess
Jacqueline Almassy

Claude Cartier, 1925-1975
≈ Rita Salmona

Anne-Marie Cartier
= René Révillon

Alain
Véronique

René Louis
Michel

Pierre-Camilla Cartier
1878–1965
= Elma Rumsey

Marion Cartier
= Pierre Claudel

Violaine
Dominique
Elma
Marie
Michèle
Pierre

Jacques-Théodule Cartier
1884–1942
= Nelly Harjes

Jacqueline
Alice
Jean-Jacques
Harjes

Suzanne Cartier
= Jacques Worth,
son of Gaston Worth

Roger
Hélène
Maurice
Gérard

CARTIER'S CHRONOLOGY

1847	Foundation of Cartier, 29, rue Montorgueil, Paris
1853	Transfer to 5, rue Neuve-des-Petits-Champs
1859	Transfer to 9, boulevard des Italiens
1871-73	Temporary branch in London
1899	Transfer to 13, rue de la Paix, Paris
1902	Foundation of branch at 4 New Burlington Street, London
1908	Temporary branch at 28, quai de la Cour, St. Petersburg
1909	Transfer to 175/76 New Bond Street, London
1909	Opening of New York at 712 Fifth Avenue
1912	13, rue de la Paix extended to 11, rue de la Paix
1917	Transfer to 653 Fifth Avenue
1929	Branch at St. Moritz
1935	Opening of Monte Carlo
1938	Opening of Cannes
1940	Temporary shop in Biarritz (during the German occupation of Paris)
1945	Pierre Cartier President of Cartier International

1962	New York sold by Claude Cartier
1966	Paris sold by Marion Cartier
1969	Opening of Geneva
1969	Opening of Hong Kong
1971	Opening of Munich
1972	A group of investors organized by Joseph Kanouï acquire control of Paris. Appointment of Robert Hocq as President and Alain D. Perrin as Marketing Manager
1973	Creation of "Les Must de Cartier"
1973	First "Must" boutiques in Biarritz, Singapore, Tokyo
1976	Acquisition of New York by another group of investors. Appointment of Joseph Kanouï as Chairman
1979	Birth of "Cartier World" through the merger of the groups owning Paris, London and New York
1984	Opening of Milan
1984	Opening of Rome
1986	Opening of Zurich
1986	Opening of Berlin

We wish to advise the visitors of the Cartier Museum exhibition to refer to Hans Nadelhoffer's book "Cartier - Jewelers Extraordinary" published by Thames and Hudson.